RISING ★ STARS

ASSESSMENT

Grammar, Punctuation and Spelling

Progress Tests

Year

6

Marie Lallaway

Series Advisors: Cornwall Learning

Rising Stars UK Ltd, 7 Hatchers Mews, Bermondsey Street, London SE1 3GS

www.risingstars-uk.com

Published 2014
Reprinted 2014 (five times), 2015 (three times)

All facts were correct at time of going to press.

The right of Marie Lallaway to be identified as the author of this work has been asserted by her in accordance with the Copyright, Design and Patents Act 1998.

Author: Marie Lallaway
Series Editor: Maddy Barnes
Educational consultant: Sara Moult
Editorial: Sarah Davies, Lesley Densham for Green Desert Ltd and Dodi Beardshaw
Accessibility reviewer: Vivien Kilburn
Design: Andy Wilson for Green Desert Ltd
Cover design: Burville-Riley Partnership

Rising Stars is grateful to the following people and schools who contributed to the development of these materials: Plumcroft Primary School, London; St Helens Teaching Schools Alliance; St Margaret's CE Primary School, Heywood, Rochdale; Tennyson Road Primary School, Luton

British Library Cataloguing in Publication Data.
A CIP record for this book is available from the British Library.
ISBN: 978 1 78339 135 6

Printed by Ashford Colour Press Ltd.

Contents

Introduction

Why use Rising Stars Assessment Progress Tests?

The *Rising Stars Assessment Grammar, Punctuation and Spelling Progress Tests* have been developed to support teachers assess the progress their pupils are making against the grammar, spelling, vocabulary and punctuation requirements of the 2014 National Curriculum Programme of Study for English in Years 2 to 6. Separate progress tests are available to cover the requirements for reading. For Year 1 there is a single set of progress tests for English. All *Rising Stars Assessment Progress Tests* are designed to support effective classroom assessment and are easy to use and mark.

The *Rising Stars Assessment Grammar, Punctuation and Spelling Progress Tests* include separate half-termly tests for spelling and for grammar, punctuation and vocabulary. All the tests have been:

- written by primary English assessment specialists
- reviewed by primary English curriculum and assessment experts.

How do the tests track progress?

The results data from the tests can be used to track progress. They show whether pupils are making the expected progress for their year, more than expected progress or less than expected progress. This data can then be used alongside other evidence to enable effective planning of future teaching and learning, for reporting to parents and as evidence for Ofsted inspections. If teachers are using the CD-ROM version of the tests, the results data can be keyed into the Progress Tracker (see pages 6–7 for more information) which automatically shows the progress of individual pupils against the Programme of Study and the results for all pupils by question and test. Data can also be exported into the school's management information system (MIS).

About the Grammar, Punctuation and Vocabulary and Spelling Progress Tests

The tests are written to match the requirements of the Programme of Study for the 2014 National Curriculum including the Appendices for English. For each half term there is a grammar, punctuation and vocabulary test and a separate spelling test. The number of marks for each test is as follows:

	Year 2	Year 3	Year 4	Year 5	Year 6
Grammar, punctuation and vocabulary	10	20	20	20	20
Spelling	20	20	20	20	20

Each question in the grammar, punctuation and vocabulary test is marked G (grammar), P (punctuation) or V (vocabulary and language strategies). Further details of what the questions cover can be found in the Coverage grid on page 69.

The style of the tests mirrors that of the tests pupils will take at the end of Key Stages 1 and 2. Spellings are assessed using contextualised sentences. Questions in the grammar, punctuation and vocabulary tests use the cognitive domains derived from Bloom's taxonomy: knowledge, comprehension, application, analysis, synthesis and evaluation.

Test demand

Test demand increases both within tests and across the year, which means that tests at the beginning of the year are easier than those at the end of the year. Difficulty is also built into each test with questions increasing in difficulty as pupils work their way through. In the grammar, punctuation and vocabulary tests, questions become more demanding in terms of response type, progressing from simple 'tick/circle' the correct response to requiring pupils to give an explanation of an answer. The questions for each of grammar, punctuation and vocabulary are distributed throughout each test rather than in blocks within a test.

Tracking progress

The marks pupils score in the tests can be used to track how they are progressing against the expected outcomes for their year group. The marks for each test have been split into three progress zones:

- less than expected progress
- expected progress
- more than expected progress.

The zones for each year group are as follows:

		Zone mark range		
		Less than expected progress	**Expected progress**	**More than expected progress**
Year 2	GPV	0–5	6–8	9–10
	spelling	0–11	12–16	17–20
Year 3		0–11	12–16	17–20
Year 4		0–11	12–16	17–20
Year 5		0–11	12–16	17–20
Year 6		0–11	12–16	17–20

The table gives the mark ranges for the progress zones for each test which you can use to see how well each pupil is doing in each test. If pupils are making the expected progress for their year they will be consistently scoring marks in the middle zone of marks in the tests. The higher the mark in the zone, the more secure you can be that they are making expected progress.

How to use the Grammar, Punctuation and Vocabulary and Spelling Progress Tests

Preparation and timings

1 Make enough copies of the test(s) for each pupil to have their own copy. Note that the spelling test script containing the instructions for teachers is provided separately.

2 Hand out the papers and ensure pupils are seated appropriately so that they can't see each other's papers.

3 Pupils will need pens or pencils and erasers. Encourage pupils to cross out answers rather than rub them out.

4 There are no time limits for the tests but normal practice is to allow a minute per mark for written tests. Help with reading may be given using the same rules as when providing a reader with the DfE KS2 tests.

Supporting pupils during the tests

Before the test, explain to the pupils that the test is an opportunity to show what they know, understand and can do. They should try to answer all the questions but should not worry if there are some they can't do.

Many pupils will be able to work independently in the tests, with minimal support from the teacher or a teaching assistant. However, pupils should be encouraged to 'have a go' at a question, or to move on to a fresh question if they appear to be stuck, to ensure that no pupil becomes distressed.

It is important that pupils receive appropriate support, but are not unfairly advantaged or disadvantaged. Throughout the tests, therefore, the teacher may read, explain or sign to a pupil any parts of the test that include instructions, for example by demonstrating how to circle an answer.

With younger age groups you may also consider using the version of the test on the CD-ROM and projecting it on to a whiteboard to support a whole class or group to take the tests. You may choose to refer to the words on the whiteboard and read them aloud so that pupils can follow them on the screen and on their own test paper, and then write their answers on their papers individually.

Marking the tests

Use the detailed mark scheme and your professional judgement to award marks. Do not award half marks.

It is useful to use peer marking of test questions from time to time. Pupils should exchange test sheets and mark them as you read out the question and answer. You will need to check that pupils are marking accurately. This approach also provides an opportunity to recap on any questions that pupils found difficult to answer.

Feeding back to pupils

Once the test has been marked, use a five-minute feedback session with the pupils to help them review their answers. Wherever possible pupils should be encouraged to make their own corrections as in this way they will become more aware of their own strengths and weaknesses. Agree with each pupil what they did well in the test and what the targets are for them to improve. A template Pupil progress sheet is provided on page 8 for this purpose.

Using the Progress Tracker

The table on page 5 gives the mark ranges for the progress zones for each test, which you can use to see how well each pupil is doing in each test. If pupils are making the expected progress for their year they will be consistently scoring marks in the middle zone of marks in the tests. The higher the mark in the zone, the more secure you can be that they are making expected progress.

The CD-ROM version of *Grammar, Punctuation and Spelling Progress Tests* includes an interactive Progress Tracker, which allows you to enter the marks for each question for each test by pupil. This then automatically shows you which zone the pupil is in and also the zone distribution for the class so that you can track the progress of individual pupils and the whole class.

The Progress Tracker also enables you to review the marks for each question so that you can identify areas where some or all pupils may need further support and areas where some or all pupils are ready to be stretched further. Questions in the grammar, punctuation and vocabulary tests are mapped to the National Curriculum Programme of Study for English. The focus of the questions can be viewed by rolling over the question code below the question number.

If required, data from the tests can be exported into the school's management information system (MIS) so that it can be used alongside other data in whole school monitoring including the monitoring of specific groups of pupils, such as Pupil Premium.

Full details about the Progress Tracker are provided on the CD-ROM.

Pupil progress sheet

Name: _____ Class: _____ Date: _____

Test name: _____ Test number: _____ My mark: _____

What I did well in the test:

_____

_____

_____

What I need to do to improve:

1. _____

2. _____

3. _____

- -

Pupil progress sheet

Name: _____ Class: _____ Date: _____

Test name: _____ Test number: _____ My mark: _____

What I did well in the test:

_____

_____

_____

What I need to do to improve:

1. _____

2. _____

3. _____

8

Year 6   *Autumn test 1*

Name:	Class:	Date:

1 Tick **two** boxes to show where the inverted commas should go.

☐ ☐ ☐ ☐ ☐

Thank you all for coming to our show, announced the class teacher.

P
1 mark

---

2 Circle the prefix which will make this word have the opposite meaning.

tidy

fore-   im-   over-   un-

V
1 mark

---

3 Write **one** preposition to complete **both** sentences.

Write the preposition in the box.   _____

Please don't take any more chips _____ my plate!

You will need to read _____ page one to page nine to answer the questions.

G
1 mark

---

4 Put a tick in the correct column to show if the sentence is a statement or a command.
One has been done for you.

	Statement	Command
At midnight, the clock chimed only 11 times.	✓	
Follow that car!		
A strange figure appeared from behind the tree.		
Climb as high as you can.		

G
1 mark

/ 4
Total for this page

5 Tick the box to show where a comma should go.

☐   ☐   ☐
↓   ↓   ↓
If you enjoy comedy you should see the film that's on at the

☐
↓
cinema this week.

1 mark   P

---

6 Underline the pronoun in this sentence.

Jess wanted to make a robot model from the boxes she had found in the cupboard.

1 mark   G

---

7 Which of these sentences contains a noun phrase?

Tick **one** box.

Sam considered how to climb the tree. ☐

Sam considered how to climb the tall, old tree. ☐

Sam carefully considered how to climb the tree. ☐

Sam considered whether to climb the tree. ☐

1 mark   G

---

8 Circle the words in this sentence which should have capital letters.

tomorrow, we will visit our friend, ali.

1 mark   P

/ 4

Total for this page

9 Circle the correct verb to match the gap with the correct verb use.

Tom and Sajad _____ each other since they were six years old.

| are knowing | have known | know | will have known |

G
1 mark

---

10 Write the correct determiner ('**a**' or '**an**') for each of these words.

_____ aeroplane

_____ bicycle

_____ horse and carriage

_____ ox and cart

G
1 mark

---

11 Circle the **two** verbs in this sentence.

Yesterday, our football team played a match against another school and won!

G
1 mark

---

12 Tick the correct column to show whether the sentence is written in the present or the past tense.

	Present tense	Past tense
At my school, we all have a piece of fruit at breaktime.		
My dad makes the best chips in the whole wide world.		
Yesterday, my brother baked a fantastic chocolate cake.		

G
1 mark

/ 4
Total for this page

13 Circle the **two** nouns in this sentence.

This morning we will all go to the park to play.

G
1 mark

---

14 Write each phrase in the correct short form using apostrophes.

does not   _____

could not   _____

P
1 mark

---

15 Underline the subordinate clause in this sentence.

I would love to climb a mountain even though it would be hard work.

G
1 mark

---

16 One word is used incorrectly in this sentence.

Jake done all his homework before he went out to play.

Write the correct word here: _____

G
1 mark

---

17 Add the correct relative pronoun to this sentence.

The village _____ I live is about two kilometres from my school.

[that]   [where]   [which]   [who]

G
1 mark

/ 5
Total for this page

18 Add brackets in the correct places in this sentence.

The school canteen serves a variety of potatoes chips, roast, mashed and they all taste good!

P
1 mark

19 After working outside, the children returned all their books to Mr Froy's classroom.

Explain why an '**s**' has been used in these words.

books

_____

_____

Mr Froy's

_____

_____

G
1 mark

20 Why is the comma used in this sentence? Tick **one** box.

His mum said that he could go to the cinema, the swimming pool or the park on Saturday.

to divide the sentence in two halves ☐

to introduce speech ☐

to mark a clause ☐

to separate items in a list ☐

P
1 mark

/ 20
Total for this test

Year 6   Autumn spelling test 1: *Teacher's script*

This test should take approximately 15 minutes to complete. Tell the children you are going to read out 20 sentences to them. Each sentence has a word missing on their answer sheet. Tell the children to listen carefully to the missing word and fill it in, making sure they spell it correctly. You will read the word, then the word within a sentence, then repeat the word a third time. Now read out each question to the children as below. At the end of the test read out all 20 sentences again.

(1) **Spelling one:** the word is **allowed**.

Will you be **allowed** to come out to play later?

The word is **allowed**.

(2) **Spelling two:** the word is **immediately**.

Stop that **immediately**!

The word is **immediately**.

(3) **Spelling three:** the word is **determined**.

I am sure you are **determined** to do well.

The word is **determined**.

(4) **Spelling four:** the word is **communication**.

There are many forms of **communication** in today's world.

The word is **communication**.

(5) **Spelling five:** the word is **dessert**.

What is your favourite **dessert**, apple pie or ice-cream?

The word is **dessert**.

(6) **Spelling six:** the word is **criticise**.

Please do not **criticise** my drawing because I have tried very hard.

The word is **criticise**.

(7) **Spelling seven:** the word is **rhythm**.

The drums are making a great **rhythm** for the song.

The word is **rhythm**.

(8) **Spelling eight:** the word is **considerable**.

I have put **considerable** effort into making you this cake.

The word is **considerable**.

(9) **Spelling nine:** the word is **development**.

There will be a new housing **development** on the edge of town.

The word is **development**.

(10) **Spelling ten:** the word is **interrupt**.

It is rude to **interrupt** when someone is speaking.

The word is **interrupt**.

(11) **Spelling eleven:** the word is **stationary**.

The cars are all **stationary** at the red traffic light.

The word is **stationary**.

(12) **Spelling twelve:** the word is **accompany**.

I will **accompany** you to the airport and say goodbye.

The word is **accompany**.

(13) **Spelling thirteen:** the word is **hesitation**.

Without any **hesitation**, Hassan offered to help.

The word is **hesitation**.

(14) **Spelling fourteen:** the word is **official**.

There will be an **official** investigation into what happened.

The word is **official**.

(15) **Spelling fifteen:** the word is **conscience**.

Your **conscience** will usually direct you to do the right thing.

The word is **conscience**.

(16) **Spelling sixteen:** the word is **parliament**.

A **parliament** is where politicians discuss the issues of the day.

The word is **parliament**.

(17) **Spelling seventeen:** the word is **existence**.

Do you believe in the **existence** of fairies?

The word is **existence**.

(18) **Spelling eighteen:** the word is **plough**.

A **plough** is the equipment towed by a tractor to prepare the fields for planting.

The word is **plough**.

(19) **Spelling nineteen:** the word is **initial**.

Please write the **initial** of your first name on your badge.

The word is **initial**.

(20) **Spelling twenty:** the word is **aisle**.

The **aisle** is usually through the centre of a church.

The word is **aisle**.

Year 6   Autumn spelling test 1

You need to add the missing words to these sentences. Your teacher will read out each missing word and then the whole sentence and will then read the missing word again. You should listen carefully and then write the word in the space. Make sure you spell each word correctly.

1. Will you be _____ to come out to play later?

   1 mark

2. Stop that _____!

   1 mark

3. I am sure you are _____ to do well.

   1 mark

4. There are many forms of _____ in today's world.

   1 mark

5. What is your favourite _____, apple pie or ice-cream?

   1 mark

6. Please do not _____ my drawing because I have tried very hard.

   1 mark

7. The drums are making a great _____ for the song.

   1 mark

8. I have put _____ effort into making you this cake.

   1 mark

9. There will be a new housing _____ on the edge of town.

   1 mark

   / 9

   Total for this page

16

(10) It is rude to _____ when someone is speaking.

1 mark

(11) The cars are all _____ at the red traffic light.

1 mark

(12) I will _____ you to the airport and say goodbye.

1 mark

(13) Without any _____, Hassan offered to help.

1 mark

(14) There will be an _____ investigation into what happened.

1 mark

(15) Your _____ will usually direct you to do the right thing.

1 mark

(16) A _____ is where politicians discuss the issues of the day.

1 mark

(17) Do you believe in the _____ of fairies?

1 mark

(18) A _____ is the equipment towed by a tractor to prepare the fields for planting.

1 mark

(19) Please write the _____ of your first name on your badge.

1 mark

(20) The _____ is usually through the centre of a church.

1 mark

/ 20

Total for this test

Year 6 *Autumn test 2*

Name:	Class:	Date:

1 Tick the box to show which sentence correctly uses a colon.

Sarah has: three favourite animals: rabbits, cats and horses. ☐

Sarah has three favourite animals: rabbits, cats and horses. ☐

Sarah has three favourite animals rabbits, cats: and horses. ☐

Sarah has three: favourite animals rabbits, cats and horses. ☐

| | 1 mark | P |

2 Tick the correct column to show whether each sentence is written in the active voice or the passive voice.

	Active voice	Passive voice
All the lions were given their food at the same time.		
Each of the elephants was sprayed with water by the keeper.		
The tiger walked up and down the side of its enclosure.		

| | 1 mark | G |

3 Draw a line to match the correct question tag with each sentence to make a question.

You don't have a spare pencil,	can they?
Miss Canning is a great teacher,	do you?
The twins can't come to the swimming pool,	isn't she?

| | 1 mark | G |

4 Tick the boxes to show the sentences that are in formal language.

☐ Come on, kids.   ☐ Come along, children.

☐ I would like to buy a new bicycle   ☐ I'd like to get a new bike.

| | 1 mark | G |

| | / 4 |

Total for this page

18

5 Tick the box to show where a semicolon could be used.

☐   ☐   ☐

There was an accident at the front of the school the teachers all

☐

went out to help.

P
1 mark

---

6 Underline the modal verb in this sentence.

Our school team could win the football match if everyone plays
their best.

G
1 mark

---

7 Circle the suffix which can be used with **both** of these words.

confident   fearful

-er   -ly   -ment   -ness

V
1 mark

---

8 Underline the **two** nouns in this sentence.

The letter was lying on the table unopened.

G
1 mark

/ 4
Total for this page

9 Tick **two** boxes to show where the commas should go in this sentence.

☐   ☐   ☐   ☐   ☐
↓   ↓   ↓   ↓   ↓

My father has visited Australia China Ireland and America.

P
1 mark

---

10 Add an adverb which makes sense to this sentence.

The branches of the tree swayed _____
in the strong wind.

G
1 mark

---

11 Circle the correct prefix to add to this word.

patient

[pre–]   [im–]   [dis–]   [un–]

V
1 mark

---

12 Rewrite this sentence changing the place of the adverbial.

The robbers were caught by the police at the end of the story.

_____

_____.

G
1 mark

/ 4
Total for this page

13 Tick **two** boxes to show where the inverted commas should go.

☐   ☐   ☐   ☐   ☐

Our finest acrobats will amaze you next, announced the ringmaster.

P
1 mark

---

14 Circle the **two** verbs in this sentence.

When my next-door neighbour's dog barks at night, it wakes me up.

G
1 mark

---

15 Write the word which shows the most confidence in the gap.

James will _____ beat me in a running race, but not at skipping.

[definitely]   [perhaps]   [possibly]   [probably]

V
1 mark

---

16 Copy out this sentence adding the correct capital letters.

we are all going to alex's house to play.

_____

_____

P
1 mark

/ 4

Total for this page

17 Tick to show which sentences contain modal verbs.

	Modal verbs
Don't climb on the wall. If you fall, you might break your leg!	
All the animals escaped from the zoo.	
If I can't help you to fix your bike, my sister could try.	

1 mark   G

---

18 Circle the **two** words which are in the same word family.

write   sign   book   signature   stencil

1 mark   V

---

19 Explain why dashes have been used in this sentence.

Many people used to work inside castles – soldiers, servants, traders – and villages or towns would be built around them.

_____

_____

1 mark   P

---

20 Put the correct letter in each box to show what type of word it is pointing to.

A = Adjective   **N** = Noun   **P** = Preposition   **V** = Verb

The baby hugged the cuddly toy in her pram.

1 mark   G

/ 20

Total for this test

Year 6   Autumn spelling test 2: *Teacher's script*

This test should take approximately 15 minutes to complete. Tell the children you are going to read out 20 sentences to them. Each sentence has a word missing on their answer sheet. Tell the children to listen carefully to the missing word and fill it in, making sure they spell it correctly. You will read the word, then the word within a sentence, then repeat the word a third time. Now read out each question to the children as below. At the end of the test read out all 20 sentences again.

(1) **Spelling one:** the word is **attention**.

Listen carefully because I need your full **attention**.

The word is **attention**.

(2) **Spelling two:** the word is **cereal**.

What **cereal** do you like for your breakfast?

The word is **cereal**.

(3) **Spelling three:** the word is **affect**.

Listening to music can **affect** your emotions.

The word is **affect**.

(4) **Spelling four:** the word is **physically**.

Athletes are **physically** very fit.

The word is **physically**.

(5) **Spelling five:** the word is **fought**.

The young boxer **fought** hard to beat his older opponent.

The word is **fought**.

(6) **Spelling six:** the word is **definitely**.

I will **definitely** meet you after school.

The word is **definitely**.

(7) **Spelling seven:** the word is **leisure**.

In my **leisure** time, I read lots of books.

The word is **leisure**.

(8) **Spelling eight:** the word is **wary**.

You must be **wary** of the new hamster as it may bite.

The word is **wary**.

(9) **Spelling nine:** the word is **practice**.

Choir **practice** will take place at lunchtime today.

The word is **practice**.

(10) **Spelling ten:** the word is **sensibly**.

Please walk **sensibly** to the hall.

The word is **sensibly**.

(11) **Spelling eleven:** the word is **amateur**.

My dad is an **amateur** footballer, but I would like to be a professional.

The word is **amateur**.

(12) **Spelling twelve:** the word is **queue**.

The **queue** for the cinema stretched all along the road.

The word is **queue**.

(13) **Spelling thirteen:** the word is **exaggerate**.

Yasmin does sometimes **exaggerate** what has happened.

The word is **exaggerate**.

(14) **Spelling fourteen:** the word is **pronunciation**.

Your **pronunciation** of difficult words is excellent.

The word is **pronunciation**.

(15) **Spelling fifteen:** the word is **opportunity**.

Saman has the **opportunity** to play in the school orchestra.

The word is **opportunity**.

(16) **Spelling sixteen:** the word is **environmental**.

Global warming is an **environmental** concern.

The word is **environmental**.

(17) **Spelling seventeen:** the word is **financial**.

A **financial** advisor helps people to use their money wisely.

The word is **financial**.

(18) **Spelling eighteen:** the word is **achievement**.

Learning all your spellings is a super **achievement**.

The word is **achievement**.

(19) **Spelling nineteen:** the word is **toleration**.

We all need to show **toleration** for each other's personalities.

The word is **toleration**.

(20) **Spelling twenty:** the word is **ambitious**.

The explorer had an **ambitious** plan to climb the mountain.

The word is **ambitious**.

Year 6   Autumn spelling test 2

You need to add the missing words to these sentences. Your teacher will read out each missing word and then the whole sentence and will then read the missing word again. You should listen carefully and then write the word in the space. Make sure you spell each word correctly.

1 Listen carefully because I need your full _____.

1 mark

2 What _____ do you like for your breakfast?

1 mark

3 Listening to music can _____ your emotions.

1 mark

4 Athletes are _____ very fit.

1 mark

5 The young boxer _____ hard to beat his older opponent.

1 mark

6 I will _____ meet you after school.

1 mark

7 In my _____ time, I read lots of books.

1 mark

8 You must be _____ of the new hamster as it may bite.

1 mark

9 Choir _____ will take place at lunchtime today.

1 mark

10 Please walk _____ to the hall.

1 mark

/ 10

Total for this page

(11) My dad is an _____ footballer, but I would like to be a professional.

1 mark

(12) The _____ for the cinema stretched all along the road.

1 mark

(13) Yasmin does sometimes _____ what has happened.

1 mark

(14) Your _____ of difficult words is excellent.

1 mark

(15) Saman has the _____ to play in the school orchestra.

1 mark

(16) Global warming is an _____ concern.

1 mark

(17) A _____ advisor helps people to use their money wisely.

1 mark

(18) Learning all your spellings is a super _____.

1 mark

(19) We all need to show _____ for each other's personalities.

1 mark

(20) The explorer had an _____ plan to climb the mountain.

1 mark

/ 20

Total for this test

Year 6   *Spring test 1*

Name:	Class:	Date:

1 Circle the more formal word choice for these sentences.

rubbish / incorrect

Your answer to that question is _____.

get / take

Please _____ a new exercise book from the cupboard.

G
1 mark

---

2 Underline the words which tell you what the cat looks like.

The brown cat with the black stripes sometimes scratches people.

G
1 mark

---

3 Tick the sentence which has **two** verbs.

A bus stops just outside my house. ☐

I often walk or run to school. ☐

Miss Andrew's car is smart and sporty. ☐

The lorries rattled along the bumpy road. ☐

G
1 mark

---

4 Tick the box to show which sentence describes the trees which are 250 years old.

There are 250 year-old trees in the park. ☐

There are 250 year old trees in the park. ☐

There are 250-year-old trees in the park. ☐

There are 250 year old-trees in the park. ☐

P
1 mark

/ 4

Total for this page

5 Draw a line to match the correct prefix with these words.

mis–   integrate

over–   interpret

dis–   look

V
1 mark

---

6 Add a colon to this sentence in the correct place.

There are six people in my family two sisters, one brother, Mum, Dad and me.

P
1 mark

---

7 Underline the modal verb in this sentence.

'We could escape by digging a tunnel,' suggested one of the prisoners.

G
1 mark

---

8 Circle the correct verb forms to complete these sentences.

has taught / taught

Mr Samson _____ in this school since I first came here.

has worked / worked

Louis _____ hard all day yesterday.

have made / have maked

The little children _____ cakes to share with everyone.

G
1 mark

/ 4
Total for this page

9 Put a tick in the correct column to show if each sentence is a question or a statement.

One has been done for you.

	Question	Statement
Could you open a window for me please	✓	
How soon do you think they will arrive		
It is going to be a very cold day today		
When the snow fell, the garden became a white carpet		

1 mark

---

10 Add a semicolon to separate the two clauses below.

I have found a brilliant book I can't stop reading it.

1 mark

---

11 Tick the box to show which part of this sentence is a relative clause.

☐   ☐   ☐   ☐

| Once upon a time | there lived | a dragon | which frightened all the people. |

1 mark

---

12 Add a preposition to complete this sentence.

You will find the library _____ the supermarket and the hairdresser's.

1 mark

/ 4

Total for this page

13 Write the same word to complete **both** of these sentences.

Stand by the _____ to get warm.

If you don't work hard enough, your boss may _____ you.

| | G |
| 1 mark |

---

14 Rewrite this sentence adding commas in the correct places.

Jamila is very good at swimming basketball dancing and tennis.

_____

_____ .

| | P |
| 1 mark |

---

15 Add a conjunction to complete each sentence.

although   in order to   because

You will need to practise your spellings _____ pass the test.

The rivers are running dry _____ there has not been much rain.

I love learning to swim _____ I don't like the cold water when I first jump in.

| | G |
| 1 mark |

---

16 Tick the columns to show whether each semicolon has been used correctly or incorrectly.

	Correctly	Incorrectly
Walking in mountains can be hard work; going up and coming down.		
Deserts are difficult places to live; they can be very hot in the day and very cold at night.		
A jungle is full of many types of plants; and creatures.		

| | P |
| 1 mark |

| | / 4 |
| Total for this page |

17 Add the correct suffixes to the words in this sentence.

In my family, my sister is young_____ than me but our new baby

brother is the young_____.

V

1 mark

---

18 Rewrite the sentence changing the position of the words underlined.

The dog grew bored with chasing the cat <u>after a while</u>.

_____ , _____

_____.

G

1 mark

---

19 Tick **one** box to show which group of pronouns should complete this sentence.

The questions were so tricky that he had to ask _____ friend to help

_____ answer _____.

a	to	they	☐
he	her	those	☐
his	him	them	☐
him	them	it	☐

G

1 mark

---

20 Explain why inverted commas have been used in this sentence.

'Thank you all for coming. It has been my best ever birthday,' said Aisha.

_____

_____

P

1 mark

/ 20

Total for this test

Year 6 Spring spelling test 1: *Teacher's script*

This test should take approximately 15 minutes to complete. Tell the children you are going to read out 20 sentences to them. Each sentence has a word missing on their answer sheet. Tell the children to listen carefully to the missing word and fill it in, making sure they spell it correctly. You will read the word, then the word within a sentence, then repeat the word a third time. Now read out each question to the children as below. At the end of the test read out all 20 sentences again.

(1) **Spelling one:** the word is **convenience**.

Please come and visit us at your earliest **convenience**.

The word is **convenience**.

(2) **Spelling two:** the word is **assistance**.

My grandmother needs **assistance** to get on the bus.

The word is **assistance**.

(3) **Spelling three:** the word is **vehicle**.

You must not park your **vehicle** in front of the school gates.

The word is **vehicle**.

(4) **Spelling four:** the word is **solemn**.

The funeral was a **solemn** occasion.

The word is **solemn**.

(5) **Spelling five:** the word is **apparently**.

The mayor will **apparently** be visiting our school next week.

The word is **apparently**.

(6) **Spelling six:** the word is **attachment**.

Mrs Tester showed great **attachment** to her school by coming back to help even after she retired.

The word is **attachment**.

(7) **Spelling seven:** the word is **sacrifice**.

You will need to **sacrifice** your playtime if you do not complete your work in class.

The word is **sacrifice**.

(8) **Spelling eight:** the word is **principal**.

The **principal** aim of our work is for you to improve your spelling.

The word is **principal**.

(9) **Spelling nine:** the word is **suspicious**.

It is most **suspicious** that the milk is spilt and the cat is licking her lips.

The word is **suspicious**.

(10) **Spelling ten:** the word is **precede**.

For safety, the small children will **precede** the larger ones in leaving the hall.

The word is **precede**.

32

(11) Spelling eleven: the word is **perceive**.

Under the microscope, I could **perceive** the tiny movements of the water bugs.

The word is **perceive**.

(12) Spelling twelve: the word is **coordinate**.

Year 6 will need to **coordinate** with Year 5 to organise a treasure hunt for the younger children.

The word is **coordinate**.

(13) Spelling thirteen: the word is **innocence**.

The lawyer was trying to prove the accused person's **innocence** to the court.

The word is **innocence**.

(14) Spelling fourteen: the word is **ancient**.

There used to be an **ancient** Roman house where the library now stands.

The word is **ancient**.

(15) Spelling fifteen: the word is **cemetery**.

We regularly go to the **cemetery** to visit my great-grandfather's grave.

The word is **cemetery**.

(16) Spelling sixteen: the word is **prejudice**.

The referee seemed to prefer the red team and showed **prejudice** against the blues.

The word is **prejudice**.

(17) Spelling seventeen: the word is **disastrous**.

It was a **disastrous** day for a picnic as it rained all morning.

The word is **disastrous**.

(18) Spelling eighteen: the word is **frequently**.

Samira **frequently** helps to get the books out for the whole class.

The word is **frequently**.

(19) Spelling nineteen: the word is **persuasion**.

Dan was resisting Ahmed's **persuasion** to swap places with him.

The word is **persuasion**.

(20) Spelling twenty: the word is **borough**.

Because London is so big, it is divided into 32 areas. Each one is known as a **borough**.

The word is **borough**.

Year 6   Spring spelling test 1

You need to add the missing words to these sentences. Your teacher will read out each missing word and then the whole sentence and will then read the missing word again. You should listen carefully and then write the word in the space. Make sure you spell each word correctly.

1   Please come and visit us at your earliest _____.

1 mark

2   My grandmother needs _____ to get on the bus.

1 mark

3   You must not park your _____ in front of the school gates.

1 mark

4   The funeral was a _____ occasion.

1 mark

5   The mayor will _____ be visiting our school next week.

1 mark

6   Mrs Tester showed great _____ to her school by coming back to help even after she retired.

1 mark

7   You will need to _____ your playtime if you do not complete your work in class.

1 mark

8   The _____ aim of our work is for you to improve your spelling.

1 mark

9   It is most _____ that the milk is spilt and the cat is licking her lips.

1 mark

/ 9

Total for this page

10   For safety, the small children will _____ the larger ones in leaving the hall.

1 mark

11   Under the microscope, I could _____ the tiny movements of the water bugs.

1 mark

12   Year 6 will need to _____ with Year 5 to organise a treasure hunt for the younger children.

1 mark

13   The lawyer was trying to prove the accused person's _____ to the court.

1 mark

14   There used to be an _____ Roman house where the library now stands.

1 mark

15   We regularly go to the _____ to visit my great-grandfather's grave.

1 mark

16   The referee seemed to prefer the red team and showed _____ against the blues.

1 mark

17   It was a _____ day for a picnic as it rained all morning.

1 mark

18   Samira _____ helps to get the books out for the whole class.

1 mark

19   Dan was resisting Ahmed's _____ to swap places with him.

1 mark

20   Because London is so big, it is divided into 32 areas. Each one is known

as a _____.

1 mark

/ 20

Total for this test

Year 6 *Spring test 2*

Name:	Class:	Date:

1 Tick the **two** sentences with the correct apostrophes.

I'm sorry but I can't help you today. ☐

Simon doesn't like cat's or dog's. ☐

Natalia won't try any new food's. ☐

They hadn't been to Amir's house before. ☐

P
1 mark

---

2 Circle the word that is similar in meaning to:

seldom

alert   often   rarely   soon

V
1 mark

---

3 Tick the boxes to show the words that should have capital letters.

☐ ☐ ☐   ☐   ☐
↓ ↓ ↓   ↓   ↓

every april, we go to visit our cousins in america.

P
1 mark

---

4 The words underlined are not correct. Write the correct words on the lines below them.

They <u>done</u> the shopping and <u>was</u> soon home.

_____   _____

G
1 mark

/ 4
Total for this page

5 Tick the correct column to show whether each sentence is written in the active or the passive voice.

	Active voice	Passive voice
All of the children were given a special treat.		
The window was broken by a stone.		
Everyone was happy with the new play equipment.		

G

1 mark

6 Put the correct letter in each box to show what type of word it is pointing to.

A = Adjective   **C** = Conjunction   **N** = Noun   **P** = Pronoun   **V** = Verb

If I were rich, I would use my money to help children to learn from

education and sport.

G

1 mark

7 Tick the **two** sentences which are punctuated correctly.

I eat a lot of fruit: bananas, pears and apples. ☐

My wardrobe is full: of clothes jumpers, jeans, socks and shirts. ☐

The treasure chest was full of precious stones, diamonds, emeralds. ☐

We have plenty to do on our holiday: building sandcastles, catching crabs and paddling in the sea. ☐

P

1 mark

8 Circle the more informal word choice for these sentences.

Shall we _____ a new television?   buy / purchase

What time will you _____ here?   arrive / get

My _____ is coming to stay.   grandmother / granny

G

1 mark

/ 4

Total for this page

9 Underline the **two** words which show a command in the passage below.

Turn on the television. Sit down quickly. Your brother is on the news right now.

G

1 mark

---

10 Circle **three** nouns in this sentence.

The museum was interesting as we saw clothes and weapons from long ago.

G

1 mark

---

11 Copy the word underlined in this sentence and add the correct apostrophe.

It <u>isnt</u> fair if the green team has more players than the blue team.

_____

P

1 mark

---

12 Tick the box to show the sentence that is correctly punctuated.

It's stopped raining, let's go out to play. ☐

It's stopped raining; let's go out to play. ☐

It's stopped raining, let's go; out to play. ☐

It's stopped raining (let's go) out to play. ☐

P

1 mark

/ 4

Total for this page

13 Add a comma to this sentence.

As quickly as possible come in and take off your coats.

P
1 mark

---

14 Write **one** word which can complete **both** of these sentences.

Mind you don't _____ on the ice.

Please pass me a small _____ of paper.

G
1 mark

---

15 Circle the **two** conjunctions in this passage.

The man walked until it was dark. When he could see no more, he sat down beside a tree to sleep.

G
1 mark

---

16 Put the correct letter in each box to show what type of word it is pointing to.

A = Adjective   **P** = Pronoun   **N** = Noun   **V** = Verb

The lively puppy barked and chased its own tail enthusiastically.

G
1 mark

/ 4

Total for this page

17 Copy this sentence adding **two** commas.

Moles which may look harmless can cause problems for gardeners.

_____

_____

P

1 mark

---

18 Rewrite the words underlined to make the sentences correct.

He <u>have</u> been waiting for you for hours.   _____

I would like to <u>had</u> known you were coming.   _____

We have been <u>prepared</u> a lovely dinner for you. _____

G

1 mark

---

19 Explain why the words underlined are placed between a pair of commas.

My uncle, <u>who usually lives in New York</u>, is coming to stay with us for the summer.

_____

_____

G

1 mark

---

20 Explain how using the word '**might**' instead of '**will**' changes the meaning of this sentence.

I will come to see you tomorrow.

I might come to see you tomorrow.

_____

_____

G

1 mark

/ 20

Total for this test

Year 6   Spring spelling test 2: *Teacher's script*

This test should take approximately 15 minutes to complete. Tell the children you are going to read out 20 sentences to them. Each sentence has a word missing on their answer sheet. Tell the children to listen carefully to the missing word and fill it in, making sure they spell it correctly. You will read the word, then the word within a sentence, then repeat the word a third time. Now read out each question to the children as below. At the end of the test read out all 20 sentences again.

(1) **Spelling one:** the word is **observe**.

If you **observe** carefully, you will see the butterfly emerge.

The word is **observe**.

(2) **Spelling two:** the word is **advice**.

My best friend often gives me good **advice**.

The word is **advice**.

(3) **Spelling three:** the word is **knight**.

In the olden days, a **knight** often wore armour in battle.

The word is **knight**.

(4) **Spelling four:** the word is **interference**.

You should be able to work without **interference** from others.

The word is **interference**.

(5) **Spelling five:** the word is **application**.

Parents will need to complete an **application** form.

The word is **application**.

(6) **Spelling six:** the word is **embarrass**.

If you are rude, you may **embarrass** your parents.

The word is **embarrass**.

(7) **Spelling seven:** the word is **ceiling**.

I can nearly touch the **ceiling**.

The word is **ceiling**.

(8) **Spelling eight:** the word is **changeable**.

Oskar can be quite **changeable** and moody.

The word is **changeable**.

(9) **Spelling nine:** the word is **cooperate**.

If we all **cooperate**, we can get the job done.

The word is **cooperate**.

(10) **Spelling ten:** the word is **prophet**.

A **prophet** predicts the future.

The word is **prophet**.

(11) **Spelling eleven:** the word is **sincerely**.

Letters sometimes end with 'Yours **sincerely**'.

The word is **sincerely**.

(12) **Spelling twelve:** the word is **available**.

Please find an **available** seat and sit down.

The word is **available**.

(13) **Spelling thirteen:** the word is **transferred**.

I have **transferred** you to a new group for maths.

The word is **transferred**.

(14) **Spelling fourteen:** the word is **legible**.

Make sure your handwriting is **legible**.

The word is **legible**.

(15) **Spelling fifteen:** the word is **conscious**.

The patient became **conscious** again.

The word is **conscious**.

(16) **Spelling sixteen:** the word is **independence**.

As you grow up, you will have more **independence**.

The word is **independence**.

(17) **Spelling seventeen:** the word is **substantial**.

Eli has made **substantial** improvements in his reading.

The word is **substantial**.

(18) **Spelling eighteen:** the word is **privilege**.

You have won the story competition and will have the **privilege** of meeting a real author.

The word is **privilege**.

(19) **Spelling nineteen:** the word is **occupy**.

Puzzles and quizzes are great ways to **occupy** your mind.

The word is **occupy**.

(20) **Spelling twenty:** the word is **hindrance**.

Carrying a heavy bag can be a major **hindrance** to walking quickly.

The word is **hindrance**.

Year 6   Spring spelling test 2

You need to add the missing words to these sentences. Your teacher will read out each missing word and then the whole sentence and will then read the missing word again. You should listen carefully and then write the word in the space. Make sure you spell each word correctly.

1   If you _____ carefully, you will see the butterfly emerge.

1 mark

2   My best friend often gives me good _____.

1 mark

3   In the olden days, a _____ often wore armour in battle.

1 mark

4   You should be able to work without _____ from others.

1 mark

5   Parents will need to complete an _____ form.

1 mark

6   If you are rude, you may _____ your parents.

1 mark

7   I can nearly touch the _____.

1 mark

8   Oskar can be quite _____ and moody.

1 mark

9   If we all _____, we can get the job done.

1 mark

10   A _____ predicts the future.

1 mark

/ 10

Total for this page

11 Letters sometimes end with 'Yours _____!

1 mark

12 Please find an _____ seat and sit down.

1 mark

13 I have _____ you to a new group for maths.

1 mark

14 Make sure your handwriting is _____.

1 mark

15 The patient became _____ again.

1 mark

16 As you grow up, you will have more _____.

1 mark

17 Eli has made _____ improvements in his reading.

1 mark

18 You have won the story competition and will have the

_____ of meeting a real author.

1 mark

19 Puzzles and quizzes are great ways to _____ your mind.

1 mark

20 Carrying a heavy bag can be a major _____ to walking quickly.

1 mark

/ 20

Total for this test

Year 6   *Summer test 1*

Name:	Class:	Date:

1 Tick the boxes to show the sentences that use commas correctly.

Can you help me to move these stools chairs, and tables to the sides of the room? ☐

Please put your book, pencil and rubber on the table. ☐

We are going to draw dragons, unicorns and other imaginary creatures in our art lesson. ☐

You can find books, and magazines in the library. ☐

P
1 mark

2 Circle the correct verb forms to complete this sentence.

had / have   have slipped / slipped

I _____ been running to school when I _____

am / have been

and fell. Since then I _____ using crutches because I hurt my ankle.

G
1 mark

3 Tick **one** box to show which pair of determiners completes this sentence.

I would like to have _____ shoes, but if they don't fit, I will try _____ ones.

some   any   ☐   them   those   ☐

these   those   ☐   this   them   ☐

G
1 mark

/ 3
Total for this page

4 Tick the correct column to show whether the sentences are in the present or past tense.

	Present tense	Past tense
The fire brigade managed to put out the fire very quickly.		
When the leaves fall from the trees, my dad sweeps them up into a pile.		
As soon as he could walk, my brother followed me everywhere.		

1 mark G

5 Tick the boxes to show where the inverted commas should go.

☐ ☐ ☐

The referee blew her whistle and told the players, I will have fair

☐ ☐

play or I will send you off the pitch.

1 mark P

6 Underline the modal verb in this sentence.

Do you think it might rain today?

1 mark G

7 Tick the box to show which sentence has a relative clause.

My hamster likes to make a bed from pieces of paper. ☐

Our kittens will be opening their eyes when they are about three weeks old. ☐

The ducks which live on the lake have made nests for their eggs. ☐

The pony in the field near school has had a foal. ☐

1 mark G

/ 4

Total for this page

8

Two words in this sentence should have apostrophes.

Meet Fatima. Shes my cousin from Egypt. She speaks Arabic but she doesnt speak much English.

Copy and write the words correctly including an apostrophe for each.

_____   _____

	P
1 mark

9

Add a preposition to this sentence.

If the gate is locked, you may need to climb _____ the fence.

	G
1 mark

10

Circle the **two** conjunctions in this passage.

Salim can balance a book on his head while he stands on one leg. Whenever I try to do this, the book falls off. Maybe I don't practise enough.

	G
1 mark

11

Draw a line to show the word which means the opposite of 'contrasting'.

deceiving

different

contrasting

long–lasting

similar

	V
1 mark

12

Put the correct letter in each box to show what type of word it is pointing to.

A = Adjective   **N** = Noun   **P** = Pronoun   **V** = Verb

☐ ☐   ☐   ☐

She gave her brother a popular computer game for his birthday.

	G
1 mark

/ 5
Total for this page

13 Draw a line to match the correct question tag with each sentence to make a question.

You like pizza,	has she?
Henry could have tidied up,	don't you?
Ola hasn't finished her dinner,	couldn't he?

1 mark   G

---

14 Underline all the words that give information about what the sheep looks like.

The sheep with the black legs and a patch on its eye is my favourite one.

1 mark   G

---

15 Add the same suffix to **both** words to complete these sentences.

You need to tight_____ the knot on your shoelaces or they will come undone.

A new coat of paint will bright_____ this room.

1 mark   V

---

16 Add a semicolon to separate these clauses.

The explorer discovered a new plant it was named after her.

They climbed to the top of the mountain the view was amazing.

1 mark   P

/ 4

Total for this page

17 Rewrite this active sentence using the passive voice.

The dog ate all my biscuits.

My biscuits _____.

G
1 mark

---

18 Add dashes to this sentence.

On the farm which is near our school there are pigs, goats and cows.

P
1 mark

---

19 Rewrite this sentence correctly.

He were the first person I met when I come to this school.

_____

G
1 mark

---

20 Explain why a colon is used in this sentence.

In the summer, we will visit a number of people in our family: aunts,

uncles, cousins and grandparents.

_____

_____

P
1 mark

/ 20

Total for this test

Year 6   Summer spelling test 1: *Teacher's script*

This test should take approximately 15 minutes to complete. Tell the children you are going to read out 20 sentences to them. Each sentence has a word missing on their answer sheet. Tell the children to listen carefully to the missing word and fill it in, making sure they spell it correctly. You will read the word, then the word within a sentence, then repeat the word a third time. Now read out each question to the children as below. At the end of the test read out all 20 sentences again.

1 **Spelling one:** the word is **steel**.

The bridge was held up by strong **steel** wires.

The word is **steel**.

2 **Spelling two:** the word is **enjoyable**.

An ice-cream on a hot day is an **enjoyable** treat.

The word is **enjoyable**.

3 **Spelling three:** the word is **terribly**.

It was **terribly** exciting waiting for my birthday to arrive.

The word is **terribly**.

4 **Spelling four:** the word is **necessary**.

Have you got all the **necessary** equipment for the game?

The word is **necessary**.

5 **Spelling five:** the word is **curiosity**.

The wrapped up box in the middle of the room was causing a lot of **curiosity**.

The word is **curiosity**.

6 **Spelling six:** the word is **yacht**.

The **yacht** had huge sails and made good speed across the open water.

The word is **yacht**.

7 **Spelling seven:** the word is **mourning**.

Berta was **mourning** the loss of her aunt who had been very special to her.

The word is **mourning**.

8 **Spelling eight:** the word is **re-enter**.

Once you leave the cinema, you may not **re-enter**.

The word is **re-enter**.

9 **Spelling nine:** the word is **preference**.

You would be my first **preference** to be captain of the team.

The word is **preference**.

10 **Spelling ten:** the word is **appreciate**.

I do **appreciate** all your help.

The word is **appreciate**.

11 **Spelling eleven:** the word is **thistle**.

There is a spiky **thistle** growing outside the window.

The word is **thistle**.

12 **Spelling twelve:** the word is **obedience**.

I am taking my dog to **obedience** classes so it will learn to behave well.

The word is **obedience**.

13 **Spelling thirteen:** the word is **decency**.

Georgina borrowed my wellington boots and had the **decency** to clean them before she returned them.

The word is **decency**.

14 **Spelling fourteen:** the word is **consideration**.

Please keep the noise down out of **consideration** for the other classes.

The word is **consideration**.

15 **Spelling fifteen:** the word is **cautious**.

The new student made a **cautious** entry into the classroom.

The word is **cautious**.

16 **Spelling sixteen:** the word is **infectious**.

Paolo's laughter was **infectious** and soon everyone was giggling.

The word is **infectious**.

17 **Spelling seventeen:** the word is **relevance**.

Ryan's comments had no **relevance** to what we were trying to discuss.

The word is **relevance**.

18 **Spelling eighteen:** the word is **committee**.

We have a student **committee** to discuss issues important to the school.

The word is **committee**.

19 **Spelling nineteen:** the word is **mischievous**.

Keisha had a **mischievous** grin on her face so we knew she was planning something!

The word is **mischievous**.

20 **Spelling twenty:** the word is **guarantee**.

I have put the **guarantee** for your new computer in the top drawer.

The word is **guarantee**.

Year 6   Summer spelling test 1

You need to add the missing words to these sentences. Your teacher will read out each missing word and then the whole sentence and will then read the missing word again. You should listen carefully and then write the word in the space. Make sure you spell each word correctly.

1. The bridge was held up by strong _____ wires.

   1 mark

2. An ice-cream on a hot day is an _____ treat.

   1 mark

3. It was _____ exciting waiting for my birthday to arrive.

   1 mark

4. Have you got all the _____ equipment for the game?

   1 mark

5. The wrapped up box in the middle of the room was causing

   a lot of _____.

   1 mark

6. The _____ had huge sails and made good speed across the open water.

   1 mark

7. Berta was _____ the loss of her aunt who had been very special to her.

   1 mark

8. Once you leave the cinema, you may not _____.

   1 mark

9. You would be my first _____ to be captain of the team.

   1 mark

/ 9

Total for this page

(10) I do _____ all your help.

1 mark

(11) There is a spiky _____ growing outside the window.

1 mark

(12) I am taking my dog to _____ classes so it will learn to behave well.

1 mark

(13) Georgina borrowed my wellington boots and had the

_____ to clean them before she returned them.

1 mark

(14) Please keep the noise down out of _____ for the other classes.

1 mark

(15) The new student made a _____ entry into the classroom.

1 mark

(16) Paolo's laughter was _____ and soon everyone was giggling.

1 mark

(17) Ryan's comments had no _____ to what we were trying to discuss.

1 mark

(18) We have a student _____ to discuss issues important to the school.

1 mark

(19) Keisha had a _____ grin on her face so we knew she was planning something!

1 mark

(20) I have put the _____ for your new computer in the top drawer.

1 mark

/ 20

Total for this test

Year 6 *Summer test 2*

Name:	Class:	Date:

1 Circle the suffix which can be used with **both** of these words.

disagree_____

fulfil_____

| -ful | | -ify | | -ly | | -ment |

1 mark V

---

2 Tick the box to show which sentence has **two** verbs.

Each day, I walk to school with my friends. ☐

In the morning, I clean my teeth and brush my hair. ☐

Tomorrow, I shall begin a new book. ☐

Yesterday, we played basketball after school. ☐

1 mark G

---

3 Circle the verbs in the past tense in this passage.

Usually, I play with my younger sister after school, but yesterday I went

to the park with my friends and we chased each other for a game.

1 mark G

---

4 Tick **two** boxes to show where commas should go to make the meaning clearer.

☐   ☐   ☐

Some sharks which can grow up to six metres long are

☐

immensely powerful.

1 mark P

/ 4

Total for this page

5 Circle the correct pronouns to complete these sentences.

Elephants look after _____ young for a long time.

his   her   our   their

A hippopotamus will protect her baby using _____ powerful jaws.

her   his   our   their

Baby giraffes learn to stand very quickly although _____ are not strong at first.

he   she   they   we

1 mark   G

---

6 Underline **two** conjunctions in this sentence.

My grandparents finally arrived although they were very late because they had been stuck in traffic.

1 mark   G

---

7 Tick the boxes to show where the commas should go.

Where I live, there is plenty of sunshine a little rain snow and lots of windy days for flying kites.

1 mark   P

---

8 Tick the correct column to show whether each sentence has a relative clause or not.

	Yes	No
Who can help to organise the party for Reception class?		
I would like to find someone who knows all the answers.		
The winner is the one who can solve all the clues first.		
Stella asked, 'Who should I work with today?'		

1 mark   G

/ 4

Total for this page

9 Tick **one** box to show which **two** pronouns will complete this sentence.

If I can't have _____ bicycle in the shop window, I would like _____ one over there.

the	that	☐
this	this	☐
that	this	☐
the	those	☐

☐ G
1 mark

---

10 Add a question mark in each box to show which sentences should be questions.

	?
Would you be able to lend me a blue pencil	
A whale is the largest creature on Earth, isn't it	
The door opened into a magical garden	
How do you think we can solve this problem	

☐ P
1 mark

---

11 Circle **one** word which should have an apostrophe.

My teachers desk is always tidy but some of the other classrooms are a bit messy.

☐ P
1 mark

---

12 Add **two** words to add more information to the noun in this sentence.

The cyclist was enjoying the speed of her _____

_____ bike.

☐ G
1 mark

☐ / 4
Total for this page

13 Tick the box to show the correct word to complete this sentence.

I am not sure if I can come tomorrow. I _____ be able to.

might ☐   used to ☐   will ☐   would ☐

1 mark   G

---

14 Add a dash to the correct place in this sentence.

The sun shone in the sky even though rain wasn't far away.

1 mark   P

---

15 Tick each sentence that contains a modal verb.

	Modal verb
The dreadful monster was ready to eat up everyone.	
A knight might just be able to save us.	
You never know what could happen.	

1 mark   G

---

16 Rewrite this sentence adding a colon.

Mrs Green teaches all my favourite lessons music, art, drama and sport.

_____

_____

1 mark   P

/ 4

Total for this page

17 Underline the more formal language to complete this passage.

Thank you for inviting me to your party.

I would love to come. / That's great.

If my mum **says it is OK / agrees**,

I will **get back to you / reply** soon.

1 mark V

---

18 Write the verb prefix that can complete **both** of these sentences into the box.

_____

I think I got the answer wrong because I _____heard the question.

Our cat is nervous because he had been _____treated before we had him.

1 mark V

---

19 Rewrite this sentence using the passive voice.

Leila and Joshua tidied the whole classroom while the others went outside.

_____

_____

1 mark G

---

20 Add information inside the brackets to tell more about the best friend.

My best friend (_____)
sits next to me.

1 mark p

/ 20

Total for this test

Year 6   Summer spelling test 2: *Teacher's script*

This test should take approximately 15 minutes to complete. Tell the children you are going to read out 20 sentences to them. Each sentence has a word missing on their answer sheet. Tell the children to listen carefully to the missing word and fill it in, making sure they spell it correctly. You will read the word, then the word within a sentence, then repeat the word a third time. Now read out each question to the children as below. At the end of the test read out all 20 sentences again.

1 **Spelling one:** the word is **muscle**.

The smallest **muscle** in your body is found in your ear.

The word is **muscle**.

2 **Spelling two:** the word is **variety**.

There is a great **variety** of rides at the fair.

The word is **variety**.

3 **Spelling three:** the word is **awkward**.

There was an **awkward** moment when no one knew what to say.

The word is **awkward**.

4 **Spelling four:** the word is **correspond**.

My nieces in Australia **correspond** with me by email and letter.

The word is **correspond**.

5 **Spelling five:** the word is **rely**.

You can always **rely** on me.

The word is **rely**.

6 **Spelling six:** the word is **equipment**.

Pack away all the play **equipment** into the cupboard.

The word is **equipment**.

7 **Spelling seven:** the word is **explanation**.

Do you have an **explanation** for your strange behaviour?

The word is **explanation**.

8 **Spelling eight:** the word is **nutritious**.

Fruit can be a healthy and **nutritious** snack.

The word is **nutritious**.

9 **Spelling nine:** the word is **incredibly**.

Gemma is **incredibly** good at tennis.

The word is **incredibly**.

10 **Spelling ten:** the word is **collaborate**.

If we all **collaborate** and work as a team, we will get the job done quickly.

The word is **collaborate**.

11 **Spelling eleven:** the word is **tolerance**.

If we all show **tolerance** to one another, we can overcome our differences.

The word is **tolerance**.

12 **Spelling twelve:** the word is **confidential**.

The doctor's report was **confidential**.

The word is **confidential**.

13 **Spelling thirteen:** the word is **sufficient**.

Is there **sufficient** fuel in our car for this long journey?

The word is **sufficient**.

14 **Spelling fourteen:** the word is **interruption**.

Mrs Hann began her speech but there was an **interruption** from the back of the room.

The word is **interruption**.

15 **Spelling fifteen:** the word is **commercial**.

A television **commercial** is used to advertise products.

The word is **commercial**.

16 **Spelling sixteen:** the word is **controversy**.

The council's decision to close the library caused a lot of discussion and **controversy**.

The word is **controversy**.

17 **Spelling seventeen:** the word is **harass**.

Do not **harass** the animals by making noises at them.

The word is **harass**.

18 **Spelling eighteen:** the word is **systematically**.

Hanna **systematically** organised her collection of shells in order of size.

The word is **systematically**.

19 **Spelling nineteen:** the word is **thoroughly**.

You need to **thoroughly** clean your teeth to keep them healthy.

The word is **thoroughly**.

20 **Spelling twenty:** the word is **alter**.

Miss Grey needed to **alter** the length of her jacket sleeves as they were too long.

The word is **alter**.

Year 6   Summer spelling test 2

You need to add the missing words to these sentences. Your teacher will read out each missing word and then the whole sentence and will then read the missing word again. You should listen carefully and then write the word in the space. Make sure you spell each word correctly.

1. The smallest _____ in your body is found in your ear.

1 mark

2. There is a great _____ of rides at the fair.

1 mark

3. There was an _____ moment when no one knew what to say.

1 mark

4. My nieces in Australia _____ with me by email and letter.

1 mark

5. You can always _____ on me.

1 mark

6. Pack away all the play _____ into the cupboard.

1 mark

7. Do you have an _____ for your strange behaviour?

1 mark

8. Fruit can be a healthy and _____ snack.

1 mark

9. Gemma is _____ good at tennis.

1 mark

10. If we all _____ and work as a team, we will get the job done quickly.

1 mark

/ 10

Total for this page

11) If we all show _____ to one another,
we can overcome our differences.

1 mark

12) The doctor's report was _____.

1 mark

13) Is there _____ fuel in our car for this
long journey?

1 mark

14) Mrs Hann began her speech but there was an

_____ from the back of the room.

1 mark

15) A television _____ is used to advertise
products.

1 mark

16) The council's decision to close the library caused a lot of

discussion and _____.

1 mark

17) Do not _____ the animals by making noises at them.

1 mark

18) Hanna _____ organised her
collection of shells in order of size.

1 mark

19) You need to _____ clean your teeth
to keep them healthy.

1 mark

20) Miss Grey needed to _____ the length
of her jacket sleeves as they were too long.

1 mark

/ 20

Total for this test

Answers and mark schemes
Autumn test 1

	Answer	Area	Mark	Extra information
1	☑ ☐ ☑ ☐ ☐ Thank you all for coming to our show, announced the class teacher.	P	1	Award 1 mark for both correct.
2	un-	V	1	
3	from	G	1	
4	<table><tr><td></td><td>**Statement**</td><td>**Command**</td></tr><tr><td>At midnight, the clock chimed only 11 times.</td><td>✓ (given)</td><td></td></tr><tr><td>Follow that car!</td><td></td><td>✓</td></tr><tr><td>A strange figure appeared from behind the tree.</td><td>✓</td><td></td></tr><tr><td>Climb as high as you can.</td><td></td><td>✓</td></tr></table>	G	1	Award 1 mark for all correct.
5	☐ ☑ ☐ ☐ If you enjoy comedy you should see the film that's on at the cinema this week.	P	1	
6	Jess wanted to make a robot model from the boxes <u>she</u> had found in the cupboard.	G	1	
7	Sam considered how to climb the tall, old tree.	G	1	
8	tomorrow, ali	P	1	Award 1 mark for both correct.
9	have known	G	1	
10	an aeroplane a bicycle a horse and carriage an ox and cart	G	1	Award 1 mark for all correct.
11	played, won	G	1	Award 1 mark for both correct.
12	<table><tr><td></td><td>**Present tense**</td><td>**Past tense**</td></tr><tr><td>At my school, we all have a piece of fruit at breaktime.</td><td>✓</td><td></td></tr><tr><td>My dad makes the best chips in the whole wide world.</td><td>✓</td><td></td></tr><tr><td>Yesterday, my brother baked a fantastic chocolate cake.</td><td></td><td>✓</td></tr></table>	G	1	Award 1 mark for all correct.
13	morning, park	G	1	Award 1 mark for both correct.
14	doesn't couldn't	P	1	Award 1 mark for both correct.
15	I would love to climb a mountain <u>even though it would be hard work</u>.	G	1	
16	did	G	1	
17	where	G	1	
18	The school canteen serves a variety of potatoes (chips, roast, mashed) and they all taste good!	P	1	
19	books: Because there are many books, not just one; to show plural Mr Froy's To show that the classroom is his; indicates possession	G	1	Award 1 mark for both correct. Accept any reasonable expression of these answers.
20	to separate items in a list.	P	1	

Autumn test 2

	Answer	Area	Mark	Extra information
1	Sarah has three favourite animals: rabbits, cats and horses.	P	1	
2	*(table — see below)*	G	1	Award 1 mark for all correct.
3	*(matching lines — see below)*	G	1	Award 1 mark for all correct.
4	Come along, children. I would like to buy a new bicycle.	G	1	Award 1 mark for both correct.
5	*(tick box answer — see below)* There was an accident at the front of the school the teachers all went out to help.	P	1	
6	Our school team <u>could</u> win the football match if everyone plays their best.	G	1	
7	-ly	V	1	
8	The <u>letter</u> was lying on the <u>table</u> unopened.	G	1	Award 1 mark for both correct.
9	*(tick box answer — see below)* My father has visited Australia China Ireland and America.	P	1	Award 1 mark for both correct.
10	Accept any reasonable answer, e.g.: wildly.	G	1	
11	im-	V	1	
12	At the end of the story, the robbers were caught by the police or The robbers were caught at the end of the story by the police.	G	1	
13	*(tick box answer — see below)* Our finest acrobats will amaze you next, announced the ringmaster.	P	1	Award 1 mark for both correct.
14	barks, wakes	G	1	Award 1 mark for both correct.
15	definitely	V	1	
16	**W**e are all going to **A**lex's house to play.	P	1	Award 1 mark for both correct.
17	*(table — see below)*	G	1	Award 1 mark for both correct.
18	sign, signature	V	1	Award 1 mark for both correct.
19	To add extra information/instead of brackets/for parenthesis.	P	1	Accept any reasonable expression of the answer.
20	*(labelling answer — see below)* The baby hugged the cuddly toy in her pram.	G	1	Award 1 mark for all correct.

Question 2

	Active voice	Passive voice
All the lions were given their food at the same time.		✓
Each of the elephants was sprayed with water by the keeper.		✓
The tiger walked up and down the side of its enclosure.	✓	

Question 3

You don't have a spare pencil, → isn't she?

Miss Canning is a great teacher, → can they?

The twins can't come to the swimming pool, → do you?

Question 17

	Modal verbs
Don't climb on the wall. If you fall, you might break your leg!	✓
All the animals escaped from the zoo.	
If I can't help you to fix your bike, my sister could try.	✓

Question 20

N — The   V — baby hugged   A — cuddly   P — in

Spring test 1

	Answer	Area	Mark	Extra information
1	incorrect, take	G	1	Award 1 mark for both correct.
2	The <u>brown</u> cat with the <u>black stripes</u> sometimes scratches people.	G	1	The word 'cat' may or may not be underlined. Award 1 mark for both correct.
3	I often walk or run to school.	G	1	
4	There are 250-year-old trees in the park.	P	1	
5	mis– → interpret; over– → look; dis– → integrate	V	1	Award 1 mark for all correct.
6	There are six people in my family: two sisters, one brother, Mum, Dad and me.	P	1	
7	'We <u>could</u> escape by digging a tunnel,' suggested one of the prisoners.	G	1	
8	has taught, worked, have made	G	1	Award 1 mark for all correct.
9	(see table below)	G	1	Award 1 mark for all correct.
10	I have found a brilliant book; I can't stop reading it.	P	1	
11	(tick on fourth box: which frightened all the people.)	G	1	
12	between/opposite; behind/next to	G	1	
13	fire	G	1	
14	Jamila is very good at swimming, basketball, dancing and tennis.	P	1	Award 1 mark for both correct.
15	You will need to practise your spellings **in order to** pass the test. The rivers are running dry **because** there has not been much rain. I love learning to swim **although** I don't like the cold water when I first jump in.	G	1	Award 1 mark for all correct.
16	(see table below)	P	1	Award 1 mark for all correct.
17	In my family, my sister is young**er** than me but our new baby brother is the young**est**.	V	1	Award 1 mark for both correct.
18	After a while, the dog grew bored with chasing the cat.	G	1	
19	his him them	G	1	
20	To indicate speech/to show Aisha is speaking/to show the words which are said.	P	1	Accept any reasonable expression of the answer.

Question 9

	Question	Statement
Could you open a window for me please	✓ (given)	
How soon do you think they will arrive	✓	
It is going to be a very cold day today		✓
When the snow fell, the garden became a white carpet		✓

Question 11

Once upon a time → there lived → a dragon → which frightened all the people. ✓ (tick above "which frightened all the people.")

Question 16

	Correctly	Incorrectly
Walking in mountains can be hard work; going up and coming down.		✓
Deserts are difficult places to live; they can be very hot in the day and very cold at night.	✓	
A jungle is full of many types of plants; and creatures.		✓

Spring test 2

	Answer	Area	Mark	Extra information
1	I'm sorry but I can't help you today. They hadn't been to Amir's house before.	P	1	Award 1 mark for both correct.
2	rarely	V	1	
3	☑ ☑ ☐ ☐ ☑ every april, we go to visit our cousins in america.	P	1	Award 1 mark for all correct.
4	did, were	G	1	Award 1 mark for both correct.
5	<table><tr><td></td><td>Active voice</td><td>Passive voice</td></tr><tr><td>All of the children were given a special treat.</td><td></td><td>✓</td></tr><tr><td>The window was broken by a stone.</td><td></td><td>✓</td></tr><tr><td>Everyone was happy with the new play equipment.</td><td>✓</td><td></td></tr></table>	G	1	Award 1 mark for all correct.
6	A P V N If I were rich, I would use my money to help children to learn from education and sport.	G	1	Award 1 mark for three or four correct.
7	I eat a lot of fruit: bananas, pears and apples. We have plenty to do on our holiday: building sandcastles, catching crabs and paddling in the sea.	P	1	Award 1 mark for both correct.
8	buy get granny	G	1	Award 1 mark for all correct.
9	<u>Turn</u> on the television. <u>Sit</u> down quickly. Your brother is on the news right now.	G	1	Award 1 mark for both correct. Also allow inclusion of prepositions 'on'/'down'.
10	museum, clothes, weapons	G	1	Award 1 mark for all correct.
11	isn't	P	1	
12	It's stopped raining; let's go out to play.	P	1	
13	As quickly as possible, come in and take off your coats.	P	1	
14	slip	G	1	
15	until, When	G	1	Award 1 mark for both correct.
16	A V P N The lively puppy barked and chased its own tail enthusiastically.	G	1	Award 1 mark for all correct.
17	Moles, which may look harmless, can cause problems for gardeners.	P	1	Award 1 mark for both correct.
18	has have preparing	G	1	Award 1 mark for all correct.
19	To indicate that extra information is being added/to show that it doesn't have to be in the sentence/that it is not part of the main clause.	G	1	Accept any reasonable expression of the answer.
20	It makes the action less certain/less likely/it may not happen/they are not so sure.	G	1	Accept any reasonable expression of the answer.

Summer test 1

	Answer	Area	Mark	Extra information
1	Please put your book, pencil and rubber on the table. We are going to draw dragons, unicorns and other imaginary creatures in our art lesson.	P	1	Award 1 mark for both correct.
2	had, slipped, have been	G	1	Award 1 mark for all correct.
3	these those	G	1	
4	(table below)	G	1	Award 1 mark for all correct.

	Present tense	Past tense
The fire brigade managed to put out the fire very quickly.		✓
When the leaves fall from the trees, my dad sweeps them up into a pile.	✓	
As soon as he could walk, my brother followed me everywhere.		✓

	Answer	Area	Mark	Extra information
5	The referee blew her whistle and told the players, ✓ I will have fair play or I will ✓ send you off the pitch.	P	1	Award 1 mark for both correct.
6	Do you think it <u>might</u> rain today?	G	1	
7	The ducks which live on the lake have made nests for their eggs.	G	1	
8	She's, doesn't	P	1	Award 1 mark for both correct. Capital letter for 'She's' is not required for the mark.
9	over/under	G	1	
10	while, Whenever	G	1	Award 1 mark for both correct.
11	contrasting — similar (deceiving, different, long-lasting)	V	1	
12	P V A N — She gave her brother a popular computer game for his birthday.	G	1	Award 1 mark for all correct.
13	You like pizza, — don't you?; Henry could have tidied up, — couldn't he?; Ola hasn't finished her dinner, — has she?	G	1	Award 1 mark for all correct.
14	The sheep <u>with the black legs</u> and a <u>patch on its eye</u> is my favourite one.	G	1	
15	-en	V	1	
16	The explorer discovered a new plant; it was named after her. They climbed to the top of the mountain; the view was amazing.	P	1	Award 1 mark for both correct.
17	My biscuits were all eaten by the dog.	G	1	
18	On the farm – which is near our school – there are pigs, goats and cows.	P	1	
19	He **was** the first person I met when I **came** to this school.	G	1	Award 1 mark for both correct.
20	To introduce/begin a list.	P	1	Accept any reasonable expression of the answer.

Summer test 2

	Answer	Area	Mark	Extra information
1	-ment	V	1	
2	In the morning, I clean my teeth and brush my hair.	G	1	
3	went, chased	G	1	Award 1 mark for both correct.
4	Some sharks [✓] which can grow up to six metres long are [✓] immensely [✓] powerful.	P	1	Award 1 mark for both correct.
5	their her they	G	1	Award 1 mark for all correct.
6	My grandparents finally arrived <u>although</u> they were very late <u>because</u> they had been stuck in traffic.	G	1	Award 1 mark for both correct.
7	Where I live, there is plenty of sunshine [✓] a little rain [✓] snow and lots of windy days for flying kites.	P	1	Award 1 mark for both correct.
8		G	1	Award 1 mark for all correct.
9	the that	G	1	
10		P	1	Award 1 mark for all correct.
11	teachers	P	1	
12	Accept any reasonable answer, e.g.: brilliant, new/extremely fast.	G	1	Award 1 mark for both correct.
13	might	G	1	
14	The sun shone in the sky – even though rain wasn't far away.	P	1	
15		G	1	Award 1 mark for both correct.
16	Mrs Green teaches all my favourite lessons: music, art, drama and sport.	P	1	
17	<u>I would love to come.</u>/That's great. If my mum says it is OK/<u>agrees</u>, I will get back to you/<u>reply</u> soon.	V	1	Award 1 mark for all correct.
18	mis-	V	1	
19	The whole classroom was tidied by Leila and Joshua while the others went outside.	G	1	
20	Accept any relevant clause or phrase, e.g.: (who is called Bethan/called Bethan).	P	1	

Question 8:

	Yes	No
Who can help to organise the party for Reception class?		✓
I would like to find someone who knows all the answers.	✓	
The winner is the one who can solve all the clues first.	✓	
Stella asked, 'Who should I work with today?'		✓

Question 10:

	?
	?
Would you be able to lend me a blue pencil	?
A whale is the largest creature on Earth, isn't it	?
The door opened into a magical garden	
How do you think we can solve this problem	?

Question 15:

	Modal verb
The dreadful monster was ready to eat up everyone.	
A knight might just be able to save us.	✓
You never know what could happen.	✓

68

Coverage grid

Note: content is listed using the STA test framework wording.

Test	Content	Number of questions
Autumn 1	Inverted commas	1
	Prefixes	1
	Prepositions	1
	Statements/Commands	1
	Commas to clarify meaning	1
	Pronouns	1
	Noun phrases	1
	Capital letters	1
	Present and past progressive continuous	1
	Determiners	1
	Verbs	1
	Tense agreement	1
	Nouns	1
	Apostrophes	1
	Subordinate clauses	1
	Subject–verb agreement	1
	Relative pronouns	1
	Punctuation for parenthesis	1
	Possessive pronouns	1
	Commas in lists	1
Autumn 2	Colons	1
	Passive and active	1
	Question tags	1
	Statements	1
	Semi-colons	1
	Modal verbs	2
	Suffixes	1
	Nouns	1
	Commas in lists	1
	Adverbs	1
	Prefixes	1
	Adverbials	1
	Inverted commas	1
	Verbs	1
	Synonyms and antonyms	1
	Capital letters	1
	Word families	1
	Single dashes	1
	Nouns/Verbs/Adjectives/Prepositions	1

Test	Content	Number of questions
Spring 1	Statements	1
	Noun phrases	1
	Verbs	1
	Single dashes	1
	Prefixes	1
	Colons	1
	Modal verbs	1
	Subject–verb agreement	1
	Statements/Questions	1
	Semi-colons	2
	Relative clauses	1
	Prepositions	1
	Nouns/Verbs	1
	Commas in lists	1
	Subordinating conjunctions	1
	Suffixes	1
	Adverbials	1
	Pronouns	1
	Inverted commas	1
Spring 2	Apostrophes	2
	Synonyms and antonyms	1
	Capital letters	1
	Tense agreement	1
	Passive and active	1
	Nouns/Verbs/Adjectives/Prepositions	1
	Colons	1
	Statements/Questions	1
	Commands	1
	Nouns	1
	Semi-colons	1
	Commas after fronted adverbials	1
	Nouns/Verbs	1
	Subordinating conjunctions	1
	Nouns/Verbs/Adjectives/Pronouns	1
	Commas to clarify meaning	1
	Present and past progressive continuous	1
	Relative clauses	1
	Modal verbs	1

Test	Content	Number of questions
Summer 1	Commas in lists	1
	Present and past progressive continuous	1
	Determiners	1
	Tense agreement	2
	Inverted commas	1
	Modal verbs	1
	Relative clauses	1
	Apostrophes	1
	Prepositions	1
	Subordinating conjunctions	1
	Synonyms and antonyms	1
	Nouns/Verbs/Adjectives/Pronouns	1
	Question tags	1
	Noun phrases	1
	Suffixes	1
	Semi-colons	1
	Passive and active	1
	Single dashes	1
	Colons	1
Summer 2	Suffixes	1
	Verbs	2
	Commas to clarify meaning	1
	Pronouns	2
	Subordinating conjunctions	1
	Commas in lists	1
	Relative clauses	1
	Question marks	1
	Apostrophes	1
	Adjectives	1
	Modal verbs	2
	Single dashes	1
	Colons	1
	Statements	1
	Prefixes	1
	Passive and active	1
	Punctuation for parenthesis	1